A Pi
of Salt

A Victorian melodrama by Kaye Umansky

Illustrations by Serena Curmi

Cast

Alice Paupesson
a match seller

Fran Paupesson
also a match seller

George Paupesson
a crossing sweeper

Mother Paupesson
an ailing seamstress,
whose eyesight is failing

Little Lenny Paupesson
the youngest,
who has a bad hangnail

Lord Shaftesbury
the famous social reformer

Scene One
Woe is Us!

A snowy street in the slums of Victorian London

Fran and Alice are trying to sell their matches to passers-by.

Fran	*(feebly)* Matches! Who'll buy my matches?
Alice	*(shivering)* Only ha'penny a box!
Fran and Alice	Mat-ches!
Fran	It's no good, Alice. Everyone's going home because of the snow. We won't get any more sales tonight. Besides, my feet have gone blue.
Alice	But we haven't sold anything! We can't even buy a crust of bread.

Fran   Ah, me! It's soup from the charity kitchen again. Oh, how tiresome it is to be poor and Victorian!

Fran and Alice   *(starting to cry)* Ah, me!

Alice   Here comes George with Little Lenny. Perhaps George has had more luck on the crossing.

Enter George, with a broom and a bag of salt for melting the snow. Little Lenny trails behind, clutching his finger.

Fran   *(hopefully)* George, our dear brother! How did you get on?

George   Everyone was in a hurry. I kept trying to put salt down to melt the snow, but people just kicked me out of the way. They're very irresponsible. The road's really slippery. Someone could get hurt.

Alice   But did you get any money?

5

Little Lenny *(boasting)* **He** didn't. But **I** sang a hymn and a lady gave me a farthing. Look! *(Shows girls farthing)*

Fran *(excitedly)* A farthing! That's enough for half a loaf. Three mouthfuls each, at least! Oh, what a feast we'll have tonight!

Alice You've forgotten. Mother said Little Lenny has to have more cream for his hangnail.

Little Lenny It's all right. I can be brave.

George I don't think that ointment does a thing. It's just melted candle grease. Mother gets it from the quack on the corner. I don't trust him. He sells bottled Thames water for bellyache.

Alice Little Lenny should go to a proper doctor. Then his finger would be all better and he can grow up to be a concert pianist, like Mother wants him to. Oh, if only we had the money!

Fran *(gloomily)* What it is to be poor!

All children Ah, me!

Little Lenny I don't want to be any trouble. I'm a good little boy. Mama says I'm a saint, especially when I sing hymns. I'm always cold and hungry, and my finger hurts. But I never complain, even though I didn't get a grand piano for my birthday like I wanted ...

All children (except Lenny) Shut up, Lenny!

George Well, there's no point in standing here in the cold. Mother will be anxious. Things are bad enough with her eyesight going and nobody bringing her clothes for mending, since she accidentally sewed up the bottoms of the schoolmaster's trousers.

Fran And the rent's due.

Alice And there's no food in the house ...

George ... which is falling down anyway, thanks to our wicked slum landlord, Clarence Darcy Sideburns, who lines his pockets at the expense of the poor.

Fran Not to mention our dear, innocent father, who is about to be shipped to Australia for pinching chicken feet, which he genuinely thought the butcher had thrown away.

Little Lenny And my poorly finger, don't forget.

George Things certainly can't get any worse.

Little Lenny My finger will, if I don't get the right cream.

Mother *(desperately, from off stage)* Children! My children! Where are you? Fran! Alice! George! Little Lenny! Disaster! Disaster has fallen upon us!

Enter Mother, staggering and wildly waving a piece of paper. She collapses on her knees in the snow. The children quickly gather round her to hear the dismal news.

Fran Mother!

Alice What's happened, Mother, dear? Tell us!

George   Has the roof caved in again?

Little Lenny   My finger hurts, Mama. But I'm being a brave boy.

Mother   *(hand to brow)* Oh, darlings! My poor, poor darlings! How can I tell you about this latest blow? It's the workhouse for us! There's nothing else for it. Look! *(Shows children piece of paper)* An eviction notice from our wicked landlord, C D Sideburns. We have until tomorrow to pay the back rent, otherwise he's turning us out into the snow. Oh, woe! Woe and doom! I've failed you! Mother's failed you! *(Starts to weep)*

Little Lenny   Oh, Mama, don't cry. Your Little Lenny's here. Shall I sing for you?

Fran   Not right now, Lenny. Get up, Mother, dear. Don't kneel in the snow.

Little Lenny   Will you kiss my poorly finger now, Mama?

George   Hush now, Lenny. Don't despair, Mother. We'll think of something.

The children help their cold, weeping mother to her feet.

Mother   Go home, my dears – while we've still got a home to go to.

Alice   Aren't you coming, Mother?

Mother	*(in a pitiful voice)* No. I shall call on Mr Sideburns and throw myself on his mercy. I'll offer my services as a seamstress. Perhaps he has some trousers that need taking up, or a shirt with a missing button. I'll even ... can I? Yes! I can! I'll even offer to wash and darn his woolly combinations!
Fran	*(tearfully)* Mother! Come home with us. Don't humiliate yourself this way.
Mother	A mother hen will do anything to protect her chicks, Fran. Now, go home. Take care of Little Lenny while I'm gone.
Little Lenny	I'll be a big, brave boy, Mama. I'll sing hymns while you're gone.
Mother	I know you will, my lamb. Come, my poor dears. Give Mother a hug.

The children hug their mother. Exit Mother, wiping the tears from her face.

Alice *(fearfully)* This is terrible! I don't want to go to the workhouse. You have to eat gruel!

Fran And they've got so many rules and regulations. There are no toys to play with – not even hoops or skipping ropes.

George We might even get separated. I hear they don't care tuppence about keeping families together.

Little Lenny They might be kind to a little boy like me – with a hangnail.

George *(with some relish)* I doubt it. I expect you'll be bullied unmercifully.

Little Lenny *(weeping)* Oh, boo-hoo! I don't want to go to the workhouse!

Off stage there are the sounds of horses' hooves, carriage wheels, whinnying and cracks of a whip.

Lord Shaftesbury *(from off stage)* Watch it, man! Stop! Arrrrgh!

The children stare at each other in horror.

George *(taking charge)* Sounds like an accident on the crossing. Wait here! This is a job for Crossing Sweeper Boy.

George snatches up his broom and bag of salt and exits at a run.

Fran Oh, how dreadful! Should we go and see if we can help?

Alice Let's leave it to George. He's the man of the family now. He'll know what to do.

Fran I do hope it's not serious.

Little Lenny Like my finger, you mean.

Fran He's coming back. There's somebody with him.

Alice Oooh. He's got a top hat. He looks like a real gentleman.

Enter George, supporting Lord Shaftesbury, who is clutching his back.

George Take it easy, mister. Here, sit on this wall a moment. Get your wind back.

Lord Shaftesbury *(sitting down)* Thank you, my boy.

Fran What happened?

George The gentleman nearly got knocked down. He lost his footing and slipped on the crossing. The coach missed him by inches. It wouldn't have happened if I'd been allowed to put salt down.

Alice Are you all right, mister?

Lord Shaftesbury I think so. A little shaken.

Fran You shouldn't be out in the cold, sir. Come on back to our house. It's just round the corner. We can't offer you brandy, but there may be a little tea left.

Lord Shaftesbury That's most kind of you, my dear.

13

George   Wait! I'll salt down the cobbles. We don't want you slipping again.

George salts the cobbles and sweeps the snow vigorously. The girls help Lord Shaftesbury to his feet.

Lord Shaftesbury   And who might my saviours be?

George   I'm George, the crossing sweeper.

Fran   I'm Fran.

Alice   And I'm Alice. Mind how you walk, sir, it's very slippery.

Little Lenny   I'm Little Lenny, and I've got a hangnail ...

Exit Lord Shaftesbury and the children.

Scene Two
Saved from the Workhouse!

The living room of the Paupessons' humble home

Enter the children and Lord Shaftesbury.

George Come in, sir. Take the weight off your feet.

Lord Shaftesbury *(sitting down in the only chair)* Thank you, George.

Fran I'll make you some tea, sir. Alice, throw the last table leg on the fire. We've got a visitor.

Lord Shaftesbury Wait! Please! Do not break up the furniture on my account.

Alice *(throwing table leg on the fire)* That's all right, mister. It's broken already.

Lord Shaftesbury looks around at the conditions the children are living in. He is noticeably shocked.

Lord Shaftesbury Don't you have coal, children?

George Oh, no. We can't afford luxuries, now our poor father's being deported to Australia.

Lord Shaftesbury Your father? Deported? For what heinous crime?

Little Lenny Chicken feet.

Lord Shaftesbury Chicken feet? *(Outraged)* They would send a poor unfortunate to the other side of the world because of a foot deformity?

Fran He hasn't **got** chicken feet.

Alice He took some. From the butcher.

All children He genuinely thought they were being thrown away.

Lord Shaftesbury *(getting really worked up)* This is monstrous! A gross miscarriage of justice!

Fran *(handing Lord Shaftesbury cup of tea)* Here's your tea, mister.

Lord Shaftesbury *(taking cup of tea)* Thank you, my dear.

Little Lenny Do you want to see my poorly finger now?

All children (except Lenny) Shut up, Lenny!

Lord Shaftesbury And where is your poor mother?

George Gone to throw herself on the mercy of our wicked landlord, C D Sideburns. He's going to evict us because we owe him back rent.

Fran She's gone to offer to sew up his trousers and wash his underwear.

Little Lenny *(in a dramatic voice)* To save us from the workhouse!

Mother *(from off stage)* Darlings! Mother's home!

All children Hooray! Mother!

The children exit to greet their mother. Lord Shaftesbury rises and walks to the front of the stage. This is his big moment.

Lord Shaftesbury *(to audience, with emotion)* Ladies and gentlemen. Can this be true? Do people really live in such deplorable conditions? A poor, honest woman, forced to send her little ones out into the dismal, snowy streets to sell matches and sweep crossings – with bare feet and an unattended hangnail! Look at the place! Hardly a stick of furniture left. No coal. No food. Not even any brandy! And all the while the idle rich live in great houses, with groaning tables and servants to fulfil their every need. Ah, me! That we should live in such times. I confess to being greatly shocked ... disgusted, in fact!

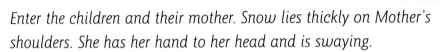

Enter the children and their mother. Snow lies thickly on Mother's shoulders. She has her hand to her head and is swaying.

Mother Why, who is this smart gentleman?

George The gentleman had an accident, Mother. He slipped on the crossing.

Mother Oh, sir. I trust you did not hurt yourself?

Lord Shaftesbury I am quite recovered, good woman. Thanks to your charming family.

Mother My babies! And to think that from tomorrow, they will have no home to go to. *(Begins to weep)*

Little Lenny Didn't Mr Sideburns want his underpants washing, Mama?

Mother No, my darling. Nothing I could say would melt his icy heart.

Little Lenny *(starting to cry)* But I don't want to go to the workhouse!

Lord Shaftesbury And, by the powers, you shall not!

Mother *(puzzled)* I beg your pardon, kind sir?

Lord Shaftesbury Madam, allow me to introduce myself. I am none other than Lord Shaftesbury, the famous social reformer. Weep no more! I shall use my considerable influence in parliament to prevent the deportation of your good husband.

The children and their mother gasp.

Mother   Can it be?

Lord Shaftesbury   Not only that! I shall also visit this despicable Sideburns fellow myself and demand that he improves your desperate living conditions. Until then, you shall live rent free!

Mother   *(joyfully)* Oh, my lord! How can we thank you? Do you hear, my darlings? We are saved!

George   And all because I didn't salt the road.

Lord Shaftesbury   A pinch of salt, that's what was lacking. And that's what we should take this play with. Ha, ha, ha!

All laugh heartily at Lord Shaftesbury's joke.

Lord Shaftesbury	George!
George	Yes, sir?
Lord Shaftesbury	Here are two guineas. *(Gives George money)* Run and purchase a bag of coal and the finest hamper you can find. It's time for a celebration!
Little Lenny	*(singing)* All things bright and beautiful ...
All (except Lenny)	Shut up, Lenny!

READY, STEADY, ACT!

This play is a melodrama. This means there are goodies, baddies, a hero and strong emotions. It pokes fun at melodrama but you should always keep a straight face.

CHOOSING THE PARTS

Who is best to play each part?

- Fran and Alice are poor, cold and hungry – but brave!
- George is cross that he hasn't been able to earn any money.
- Little Lenny sings hymns and keeps talking about his sore finger.
- Mother is desperate to care for her family.
- Lord Shaftesbury is a rich man who tries to help the poor.

Setting the scene

The play begins in a snowy street in Victorian London. How will you create this atmosphere? The children will be barefooted and shivering. Maybe some Christmas music will help. Other actors could pass them by and ignore them.

WHAT YOU WILL NEED

Costumes

The whole family is poor and ragged. Mother could have a threadbare shawl. The children will have dirty bare feet. Get their wretched clothes from jumble sales, or make them out of sacking. Lord Shaftesbury is smart and well-to-do. He could have a top hat and a cane.

Props

Make a props list from the text. George will need a broom and a bag of salt. The girls will need match boxes in a basket. A farthing is about the same size and colour as a 1p coin.

Sound effects

From offstage, we hear the noise of a carriage when Lord Shaftesbury has his accident. Use percussion instruments to make the horse sounds and maybe your voices for the whinnying.

> ### Did you know...?
> The famous fountain at Piccadilly Circus in London is a monument to the real Lord Shaftesbury. He was a Victorian politician who helped the poor in many ways.

SPEAKING AND MOVING

Speaking

All of the acting in a melodrama should be over the top – so pile on the emotions as you speak the lines. Think how the children would say, 'Ah, me!' or 'What it is to be poor!'

Lord Shaftesbury should be very serious. At some points he is outraged at the family's condition. How should he speak then?

Moving

Think how you will use your bodies to show how cold and uncomfortable the children are. Practise moonwalking on the icy pavement. Shiver a lot.

Use lots of dramatic gestures. Put the back of one hand on your forehead to show your despair.

Lord Shaftesbury comes on just after he has fallen on the ice. How might he walk?

What next?

Now you have performed this play why not:

- Invent a new scene where life is more fun – or even worse!
- Find out more about the real Lord Shaftesbury.